Guidelines for the safe investigation by drilling of
landfills and contaminated land

This document has been produced with the support of, and by representatives of, the following bodies.

Association of British Insurers

Association of Consulting Engineers

Association of Geotechnical Specialists

British Drilling Association

British Geological Survey

British Geotechnical Society

British Property Federation

British Tunnelling Society

Construction Industry Research and Information Association

County Surveyors' Society

Department of the Environment

Department of Transport

Federation of Civil Engineering Contractors

Federation of Piling Specialists

Institution of Civil Engineers

Institution of Structural Engineers

National House-Building Council

Royal Institute of British Architects

Royal Institution of Chartered Surveyors

The Geological Society

Water Services Association

4 Guidelines for the safe investigation by drilling of landfills and contaminated land

Site Investigation Steering Group

Thomas Telford, London

Publications in the **Site investigation in construction series:**

1. Without site investigation ground is a hazard

2. Planning, procurement and quality management

3. Specification for ground investigation

4. Guidelines for the safe investigation by drilling of landfills and contaminated land

Published by Thomas Telford Services Ltd, Thomas Telford House, 1 Heron Quay, London E14 4JD

First published 1993

A catalogue record for this book is available from the British Library.

ISBN 0-7277-1985-8

Classification
Availability: Unrestricted
Content: Recommendations based on best current practice
Status: Committee-guided
User: Construction industry firms and employees

Printed and bound in Great Britain

Contents

Acknowledgements

The Site Investigation Steering Group wishes to thank all the government departments, learned societies, professional associations and trade organisations for their support of this initiative, to provide guidelines to encourage improved uniform practice in site investigation for the benefit of the construction industry and its clients.

The Steering Group thanks members of the working panels and the secretariat of the Institution of Civil Engineers, who devoted much time and effort to the deliberations on which the documents are based. The Steering Group is also deeply indebted to the many organisations and individuals who provided helpful comments during the consultation period.

Executive summary

These guidelines seek to promote the use of safe working practices in the investigation of landfills and contaminated land. They are intended for use by individuals or organisations who are involved in the planning, specification, procurement, supervision and execution of such work.

For each project the objectives and anticipated hazards should be clearly defined to enable the site investigation contractor to select the appropriate plant, equipment, drilling methods, materials and protective measures for investigation of the site.

The inclusion in the contract documents of recognised conditions of contract and a Bill of Quantities are considered essential to protect the interests of Employer and Contractor. The documents should recognise statutory and contractual responsibilities, particularly with regard to health and safety, and thereby achieve a more professional contract performance.

All contractors involved in the investigation of landfills or contaminated land must carry appropriate insurances, evidence of which should be a requirement of a satisfactory tender to the Employer.

All relevant information regarding potential contamination and hazards on a site that is held by the Employer or Engineer must be provided to the Contractor at tender stage or thereafter, as soon as it comes to hand. The types of waste or contaminated ground anticipated should be categorised so that a site can be designated as GREEN, YELLOW or RED, and appropriate safe working practices employed.

A written safety plan, incorporating safety and emergency procedures, must be prepared by the Contractor prior to start of work, and all personnel on site must be given appropriate training. Recommended field operations are described in relation to drilling, sample handling, site monitoring and security. Personal protective clothing and equipment are listed, together with procedures for personnel leaving a contaminated site.

For YELLOW or RED sites, each driller should be a British Drilling Association accredited 'environmental' driller (or equivalent), capable of operating all safety equipment for the specified site designation.

It is not intended that these guidelines should replace any Acts, Codes, Regulations or other documents which have a legal or contractual force. Nevertheless, it is recommended that these guidelines should be incorporated into the contract documents in order to improve practice and safety when drilling through landfills and contaminated land.

1 General

1.1 Urgent action is required by organisations involved with landfills and contaminated land to improve awareness and understanding of their responsibilities under the provisions of the Environmental Protection Act and associated Health and Safety Regulations. There is also a growing need for drilling contractors to use appropriate drilling, sampling and testing techniques, while complying with statutory regulations to safeguard the health and safety of all personnel involved.

1.2 Owing to financial constraints, it has been observed that drillers are too often expected to recognise a hazard by either sight or smell alone. Employers should recognise the need to operate a 'safe system of working' as a main priority and not select a contractor by cost criterion only. Several Acts and Regulations (Department of the Environment (DoE), 1974, 1990; Health and Safety Executive (HSE), 1980, 1987, 1988) put the necessary onus on Engineer and Contractor to undertake work in such a manner that personnel, third parties and the environment are properly protected

1.3 As a result of the significant increase in drilling operations on landfill sites and contaminated land the following guidelines have been produced to promote safe working practices for the protection of drilling personnel and the general public

1.4 This document is intended to provide guidance for Employers, Contractors, Engineers and individual drillers (the definitions of Employer, Contractor and Engineer used in this document are those given in the ICE Conditions of Contract for Ground Investigation (Institution of Civil Engineers (ICE), 1983). However, specific advice such as the deleterious or hazardous effects of particular contaminants is not given, and this additional information should be obtained from appropriate technical references (see Suggested reading below). The following guidelines do not relieve anybody of their responsibility to consult the various Acts, Regulations and Standards that are relevant.

1.5 Any reference in this document to a UK standard, specification or accreditation body shall be construed equally as reference to an equivalent one.

2 Project requirements (Specification)

2.1   The objectives of an investigation of a project should be clearly defined to enable a Contractor to select appropriate plant and equipment, determine drilling methods, choose satisfactory materials and provide appropriate protective measures for investigation of the site. Unless the investigation is carried out solely to assess contamination, it should be designed to satisfy both geotechnical and environmental objectives.

2.2   The scope of drilling typically required for landfills and contaminated land includes site investigation boreholes, probeholes, monitoring and sampling boreholes, gas venting boreholes, leachate sampling wells and gas abstraction wells. There is usually a range of borehole diameters available and the depths, methods of construction and choice of permanent lining and instrumentation materials may vary significantly from Contractor to Contractor. It is essential therefore to determine at the precontract stage, the specific requirements for each project.

2.3   Site accessibility, safety requirements, nature of materials to be drilled, final hole diameter, hole stability, type and quality of sampling and in situ testing, cross-contamination, borehole installations and final surface completion are aspects of a drilling programme requiring careful consideration before commencement of the work.

2.4   A conflict of interest can occur when a low-cost method of drilling does not, for example, provide an accurate assessment of ground conditions, or perhaps allows cross contamination of solids or fluids. Alternative, more costly drilling techniques may be necessary to achieve all the objectives of an investigation.

3 Contractual requirements (Conditions of Contract)

3.1 In many cases within the construction industry it has been observed that contractual relationships between Employer and Contractor are informal, particularly in respect of fundamental aspects of the work such as the legal responsibilities of both parties, insurance, supervision and direction of the work, workmanship, materials, programme and safety. This can lead to strained relationships should anything go badly wrong.

3.2 The inclusion of recognised Conditions of Contract into the contract document is considered essential, firstly to protect each party's interests in a project, by identifying specific risks or hazards, recognising statutory and contractual responsibilities particularly with regard to health and safety; and secondly, to promote and achieve a more professional contract performance. A number of documents exist to provide a satisfactory contract e.g. ICE Conditions of Contract (ICE, 1983, 1991). Subcontractors should be subject to similar conditions.

3.3 The tender documents should state all the contaminants that are known to be present on the site and provide all available relevant information, which should be sufficient to enable the Contractor to assess the risks at tender stage. In turn, this information should also be forwarded by the Contractor at tender stage to any potential subcontractors

3.4 Special care should be taken to define adequately the respective responsibilities of the Employer and Contractor, when the Employer does not own the site(s) to be investigated, i.e. the Employer is prospecting the site(s) with permission of the owner for temporary possession

4 Bill of Quantities

4.1 The Bill of Quantities should allow for the Contractor to provide whatever preliminary items are considered necessary for a project, including appropriate insurance, health and safety equipment, office and stores, mobilisation of plant, equipment and personnel and any other items such as communication, statutory obligations and services for the Employer's representative. The Bill of Quantities should clearly identify the provision of suitably experienced environmental scientists, as determined by the site category (see Section 5), or as otherwise required.

4.2 Sufficient time should be allowed for tendering, so that appropriate consideration can be given to the hazards posed by a particular site and the protective measures that will be required.

4.3 In some cases it is reasonable to require the Contractor to allow for preliminary items in the Bill of Quantities for monitoring and guarding against a specific hazard or contaminant. However, it is unreasonable for the Contractor to need to allow for controlling that hazard since this will be dependent on the site and ground conditions encountered. In these situations a suitable clause to this effect should be included in the contract, and the action to be taken prior to the hazard being revealed should be stipulated (e.g. an inspector from the Health and Safety Executive should be consulted, and the method of handling the hazardous material agreed in advance).

4.4 The itemised measurement of drilling should include provision for incorporating any changes to the initially adopted drilling methods, such as sampling and testing methods which may arise as a direct consequence of unexpected materials being encountered. The provision of safety equipment on site should be included in the preliminary items but the use of individual items as required should be identified within the Bill of Quantities. Appendix II shows a range of additional items which should be included in the Bill of Quantities in order to cover landfills and contaminated land.

5 Insurance

5.1 All contractors or subcontractors involved in the drilling of landfills or contaminated land must carry appropriate insurances. Provision by the Contractor of the Certificate of Insurance should be a requirement by the Employer, in evidence of a satisfactory tender

5.2 In general, insurers consider that any work on landfills and contaminated land presents an increase in risk to drilling contractors, and parties that may be affected by their operations. The non-disclosure of the nature of the investigation may invalidate the cover, and it is therefore recommended that drilling contractors should notify their insurers before they commence such work. Evidence that this has been done and acknowledgement by the insurer should be obtained by the Employer

5.3 The majority of insurers currently apply endorsements to existing insurances in respect of investigation of pollution and contaminated land. Most insurers produce their own specific wording but in general, the cover for pollution is restricted to identifiable, sudden and unforeseeable incidents which occur in their entirety at a specific time and place during the policy period. It is essential that the detailed wording of any such conditions be examined by the Employer to ensure appropriate cover has been obtained.

6   Hazard assessment

Information 6.1
6.1.1   All relevant information regarding potential contamination and hazards present on a site or sites that are in the possession (or temporary possession) of the Employer or the Engineer must be provided to the Contractor at tender stage. Under the COSHH Regulations (HSE, 1988) the Employer has a legal responsibility to provide these details. If a hazard assessment has been carried out it is the Employer's responsibility to make a copy available to the Contractor. A suitable form on which the required information can be entered into the contract documentation is given in Appendix IV (sheets 1 to 3). The Contractor must then take into consideration the information provided when preparing a tender submission.

6.1.2   The above does not relieve the Contractor of any legal duties or responsibilities with respect to the health and safety of employees. If the Employer or Engineer cannot or will not provide the necessary information then the Contractor should take reasonable steps to acquire the information and be reimbursed accordingly.

6.1.3   The completion and submission of Appendix IV to the Contractor at tender stage will determine, by reference to Appendix V, the safety equipment to be provided at the commencement of the work, and enable the Contractor to select the most appropriate drilling method(s) to achieve the objectives of the contract in a safe practicable way.

**Categorisation of the site or 6.2
site areas**
6.2.1   The types of waste or contaminated ground either known or likely to be found on a site should be categorised so that the associated degree of hazard can be clearly recognised. Appendix III presents a colour coding system (GREEN, YELLOW or RED) which can be applied to both landfills and contaminated land.

6.2.2   It should be borne in mind that indiscriminate dumping (or in the case of older sites, uncontrolled tipping) may have taken place, and therefore the categorisation schedule must be treated only as a guide to determining operational procedures.

6.2.3   There are certain sites where initially there may be inadequate information to determine whether hazardous materials could be present. Pre-1974 non-licensed landfill sites would be an example of this. Many of these sites contain mainly ash, but there is always the possibility that indiscriminate dumping of hazardous materials has taken place. In these situations a desk study should be undertaken, possibly followed by limited probing and sampling carried out under a temporary RED designation to permit a correct site designation prior to the main drilling work. In the absence of such a procedure or where this initial appraisal does not guarantee an absence of hazardous materials then the site should be given a RED designation until the nature of the site is proved.

6.2.4   There are also many derelict sites for which the degree of contamination is not known, but significant contamination may nevertheless exist. All derelict land should be considered as suspect, and a desk study (including probing and sampling under a temporary RED designation, if appropriate) should be carried out initially to establish the correct site designation.

Gases 6.3
6.3.1 Gas generated from landfill may be encountered while drilling in landfill sites, and in some cases on contaminated sites that have been filled. Landfill gas usually contains methane, which is flammable and explosive (when in confined spaces), and carbon dioxide which is an asphyxiant. Hydrogen sulphide may be encountered on certain sites and is toxic at even very low concentrations. At very low concentrations hydrogen sulphide can be recognised by a powerful offensive smell, but the toxicity increases very rapidly as concentrations increase. Exposure to this gas for an extended period deadens the senses, such that the odour can no longer be detected, and personnel are then at serious risk.

6.3.2 Methane can be explosive at concentrations generally between 5% and 15% by volume in air. The level of 5% is referred to as the Lower Explosive Limit (LEL). Drilling operations should stop when concentrations at the surface exceed the specified acceptable limit, and should not restart until either natural or artificial ventilation has reduced concentrations to below this acceptable limit, or the borehole has been purged. The acceptable limit normally quoted is 20% LEL (1% by volume), but for drilling in the open an acceptable limit of 60% LEL (3% by volume) is likely to be more practical. Petrol-driven plant or vehicles should not be used on sites where flammable gas is likely to be encountered. Hydrogen sulphide is flammable between 4.3% and 45.5% by volume in air, and similar limiting criteria should be applied to provide safe working conditions.

6.3.3 If gas is likely to be a problem on a particular site, gas monitor(s) able to read the level of gases such as methane, carbon dioxide and hydrogen sulphide, should be available to permit regular checks during drilling (e.g every metre of hole) and immediately following any occurrence during drilling which would suggest gas emission. When drilling in the open, monitoring for carbon dioxide is not essential, but carbon dioxide constitutes a hazard in confined spaces. If working in a confined space cannot be avoided then monitoring for carbon dioxide will be required (see also Clause 7.3.8).

6.3.4 Extreme care should be taken when drilling to investigate hydrocarbon contamination caused by leakages from underground storage tanks or pipelines. Petroleum vapours, for example, are particularly hazardous and are flammable between 1% and 7% by volume in air. Liquid products can often be found floating on the surface of groundwater. Where hydrocarbon contamination is likely to be present, suitable monitoring equipment should be available on site and used in a similar manner to that described in Clause 6.3.3 above.

6.3.5 Biological and bacteriological risks may be present on certain sites. For example, anthrax can be present on any site where animal carcasses have been buried, stored or used. For such sites, practical guidelines are provided by MAFF (Ministry of Agriculture, Fisheries and Food (MAFF), 1991) and at least one month before commencing investigation work the Employer or Engineer should make contact with the MAFF Divisional Veterinary

Officer (DVO) and the Senior Plant Health and Seeds Inspector (or in Scotland, the Principal Agricultural Officer) for the site concerned. If a buried carcass is discovered, work at this location must stop immediately and advice on appropriate actions should be sought from the DVO.

6.3.6   On the above sites good personal hygiene is required to ensure that spores do not enter cuts or scratches to the skin. Anthrax can also be contracted by the inhalation of spores so masks should be worn. Other examples of hazardous sites include abandoned sewerage plants and industrial works which involve biological or bacteriological processes.

Other contaminants 6.4
6.4.1   Former explosives factories and magazines or areas where wartime activities took place could contain explosives. There are well-established procedures for dealing with explosives and munitions. In the first instance the police should be contacted who may then call in the Explosives Ordnance Disposal Unit from the armed forces.

6.4.2   The presence of radioactive materials on a site may be indicated and/or detected by a suitable detector. In such circumstances, contact should be made immediately with the police. Reference should be made to other Acts and Regulations (DoE, 1960; HSE, 1985; British Standards Institution (BSI), 1985).

7 Health and safety

Preparation 7.1
7.1.1 For general guidance on the management of safety on investigation sites and safe drilling practice, reference should be made to other publications (Association of Geotechical Specialists (AGS), 1992a, b; British Drilling Association (BDA), 1992).

7.1.2 When preparing a tender the drilling contractor should add any safety proposals not already included within the documentation but which he considers are appropriate, possibly from specific knowledge of the site. The Contractor should indicate whether such safety proposals have been included within the tender price or whether they constitute an additional cost. The safety equipment provided on site should include, but should not be limited to, those items listed in Appendix V.

Safety plan 7.2
7.2.1 A written safety plan incorporating safety and emergency procedures should be prepared prior to the commencement of work. All personnel working on the site should be given an induction on the contents of the safety plan and must acknowledge receipt of a copy. In this regard, all site staff must receive instruction on the nature of the known contaminants, the potential hazards and health risk and safety/first aid precautions. Before commencement of drilling operations the Contractor's staff must also be given in writing the telephone numbers and locations of emergency services on and off the site, including the nearest casualty department, and the location of the nearest clean water supply. This information must be kept on site and available at all times when staff and visitors are on site. Where appropriate, the information provided shall receive the prior approval of the site manager.

7.2.2 The leading driller is responsible for all safety equipment and must ensure that it is readily accessible and fully functional at a safe location near the area of drilling operations.

Site practice 7.3
7.3.1 There must always be a minimum of two drilling operators in attendance at each rig when it is working. Where possible, rigs should be positioned up-wind (in respect of the prevailing wind direction) of the borehole location.

7.3.2 All YELLOW and RED sites should be designated 'no smoking' areas, since smoking can result in the ingestion of contaminants.

7.3.3 If the borehole construction has not been completed by the end of a shift, the hole should be covered with a suitable plate such that the hole is not accidentally accessible to the public or other workers on the site. At the beginning of the next shift the rig should not be started until the plate has been carefully removed and the borehole monitored for gases.

7.3.4 Any 'hot work' (e.g. welding or burning) or potential source of ignition must be located away from any risk of contact with landfill gas, in an area off site and preferably with the authority of a site manager, who should issue a permit to work.

7.3.5   Strict personal hygiene should be promoted at all times. Contaminants may enter the body by skin penetration, skin absorption, ingestion or inhalation. Great care must be taken to eliminate these possibilities.

7.3.6   Where specified, an appropriate decontamination unit should be provided either by the Employer or by the Contractor at a suitable location at the edge of the contaminated area. A boot wash should be situated adjacent to the decontamination unit.

7.3.7   No consumption of drink or food should be permitted within the contaminated area. Any messing facilities provided should be located at a 'clean' de-restricted area, and should only be used by personnel following the removal of protective clothing, gloves, boots, etc., and washing either within the contaminated area or within a decontamination unit.

7.3.8   In the case of landfills (or any other sites where there is a potential for gas to be generated) temporary offices, huts and storage containers should not be located where infiltration of gas could occur.

Plant and equipment 7.4
7.4.1   All plant and equipment should comply with the current safety legislation, e.g. the Health and Safety at Work etc. Act (DoE, 1974), COSHH Regulations (HSE, 1988), the Noise at Work Regulations (HSE, 1989a), and the Electricity at Work Regulations (1989b).

7.4.2   Spark arrestors and automatic air intake shutdown valves should be provided on all plant and equipment operating on or near landfill sites.

7.4.3   Rig prime movers and personnel should operate as far away from each borehole as is practicable. In particularly hazardous situations, consideration should be given to remote control operation of the rig.

Recognition and treatment of 7.5
hazards
7.5.1   All personnel working on a landfill should be given advice on the recognition of diseases associated with landfills such as leptospirosis (Weil's disease), tetanus, etc. Likewise, advice should be given on the health hazards associated with contaminated land. Organisations involved with such sites should operate health surveillance schemes to ensure regular monitoring and updating of inoculations, etc.

7.5.2   All plant and equipment should be cleaned within a designated cleaning zone using steam, hot water or high-pressure water cleaning systems whenever leaving the site or a contaminated area (see also Clause 10.7 for disposal of wash water). In this regard, high-pressure water cleaning systems can give rise to mists (aerosols) containing hazardous particles, either derived from the contaminants present on site, or perhaps from bacterial or other microbiological contamination of the cleaning water itself. Operatives should wear suitable protection to prevent inhalation of aerosols and airborne particles. Eye protection is also recommended.

7.5.3   Exposure to potential hazards where the contaminants are not yet identified should be limited to the minimum practicable. Should unknown or suspicious contaminants be encountered, such as discharge of gases or unusual arisings or colouration, the drilling operations should cease immediately until an environmental health officer or environmental specialist can inspect, monitor and determine what the contaminant is and whether a hazard exists. In the case of GREEN or YELLOW sites, the hazard identified may lead to a redesignation of the site.

7.5.4   If any person on the site feels unwell this should be brought to the immediate attention of the supervisor who may then need to take appropriate action, such as obtaining medical advice and/or stopping the work. Where concern is not alleviated, an environmental health officer should be consulted about the site conditions before work continues.

7.5.5   All personnel should be alert to the symptoms of fatigue and heat stress and their effect on the normal caution and judgement of people.

Personal responsibilities **7.6**   All employees of the Contractor and all self-employed persons should be fully aware of their legal responsibilities under the Health and Safety at Work etc. Act and relevant Regulations. Such personal responsibilities have precedence over contractual responsibilities.

8 Personnel

8.1 For YELLOW or RED sites (see Section 5) each driller should be a British Drilling Association (BDA) accredited 'environmental' driller (or equivalent) and capable of operating all safety equipment for the specified site designation. Accreditation as an 'environmental' driller should include third party certification as follows.

(a) Accreditation by the BDA as a 'Ground Investigation Driller', or alternatively, have attained accredited status for the following
documentation
health and safety
boring and/or drilling
groundwater observation and instrumentation
borehole backfilling.

(b) Competence to operate the following equipment
respiratory equipment
fire extinguisher
gas detection equipment.

(c) Registration as qualified in first aid

(d) Competence to carry out routine hazard monitoring by sight, smell and instrumentation.

(e) Familiarity with appropriate protective measure.

Drilling helpers or assistants should also have received relevant 'environmental' training and be able to recognise routine hazards and administer basic first aid.

8.2 A qualified environmental scientist possessing relevant experience should be employed on every site that has a RED site designation. This specialist may also be required on YELLOW sites subject to the accuracy of documentation for the particular site. If there is doubt about the accuracy of documentation the site should be designated RED.

8.3 An environmental scientist should have suitable training and experience to enable recognition, by sight, smell or in situ test (where this is possible), of a previously unidentified hazard, and be able to incorporate any necessary changes to the working procedures to maintain a safe system of work. However, the Employer and the Contractor should recognise that some contaminants can only be identified using analytical laboratory techniques, and such testing may entail delay and additional cost to the works.

9 Field operations

9.1   A description of various techniques available for boring and drilling in landfills and contaminated land is given in Appendix I.

9.2   Arrangements should be made for the disposal of all surplus materials arising from a borehole prior to the commencement of work. This may include transfer of spoil to a licensed tip. Analysis of the spoil and appropriate documentation may be required before taking contaminated material off-site (Lord, 1987).

9.3   Extreme care is required to ensure that cross-contamination does not occur either between boreholes or as a borehole is deepened. Equipment must be cleaned between boreholes and, where appropriate, between strata in a borehole in order, for example, to avoid carrying contamination down into an aquifer.

9.4   A site-specific protocol should be prepared for the taking of samples (Hobson, 1993). The following clauses regarding safety are intended as general guidance only.

9.5   Samples obtained from boreholes must be clearly labelled and colour-coded (in accordance with site designation) to indicate the nature and category of material contained. This is particularly important for transfer of samples to a laboratory for further examination and testing, or to a licensed site for disposal. Hazardous samples must be suitably contained to ensure that no leakage or spillage can occur. Where appropriate, contaminated and potentially contaminated samples should be loaded into storage boxes for transport to the laboratory.

9.6   Contaminated or potentially contaminated samples should be stored on site, or at the laboratory, in a marked and secured area with a sign saying 'Danger: contaminated samples'. This would normally be outside unless there is a serious danger or risk to children or the general public.

9.7   Prior notice both verbally and in writing (e.g. by fax) should be given to the laboratory when any contaminated samples are being despatched to the laboratory from the site.

9.8   Special arrangements may be required for the transport of hazardous samples (HSE, 1984, 1986, 1990). Certain samples from contaminated sites must by law be carried on a marked vehicle which displays two orange rectangular plates with black borders.

9.9   If hazardous materials are found or suspected to be present on a site, then the site must be made secure at all times, day and night. There may be a need to maintain strict control of visitors by a mandatory system of signing in and out. This is essential if tests subsequently indicate the presence of hazardous material which will require that all contacts be traced for screening.

9.10   Care should be exercised in the choice of casing for permanent or semi-permanent boreholes in landfills or contaminated land, bearing in mind the contaminants at the site and the long-term objectives of the project. For example, stainless steel is unsuitable in low pH environments, and PVC is not suitable where low-level organic contaminants are present and groundwater sampling is required.

9.11   The drilling medium used should be carefully selected and controlled. For example the use of air flush should be discouraged where there is a risk that hazardous materials could be sprayed or otherwise propelled into the air. Where water is used care should be taken in respect of its origin. If there is any doubt, mains water should be brought onto site. If bowsers are used for this purpose the previous use of these should be established to ensure that they have not been previously used for fuel oils.

9.12   With the increase in the number of contaminated sites now being investigated it is necessary to consider whether equipment arriving on a site may have been contaminated by usage on a previous site. If in doubt, all plant and equipment should be cleaned on arrival.

9.13   The site must be left in a satisfactory and safe condition. For example, contaminated spoil from the boreholes must not be left exposed on the ground surface, and any boreholes that penetrate seals or low-permeability layers must be appropriately resealed to maintain the integrity of the site.

10 Protective clothing and equipment

10.1   Strict adherence to the requirements for protective clothing is essential for a contaminated site. A list of basic Personal Protective Equipment (PPE) is given in Appendix VI. This list is not exhaustive and other PPE may be required for a particular site. For example, latex inner gloves and chemical protective (e.g. vinyl or neoprene rubber) outer gloves will be required if leachate, or otherwise contaminated fluids, are likely to be encountered.

10.2   The proper level of protection should be donned before entering the contaminated area by both operational and supervisory staff.

10.3   Gloves should be worn whenever it is necessary to contact or handle waste, wet soil, ground water or any other potentially contaminated implements, materials or samples.

10.4   The level of protective clothing should be upgraded if there is any likelihood of external dermal (skin) exposure to unknown contaminants or to substances known to be toxic via the skin.

10.5   Personnel leaving a contaminated zone and entering a clean zone should observe the following procedure. Scrub boots and outer gloves using water and biodegradable non-phosphate detergent. Rinse boots and outer gloves using potable water. Remove boots. Remove and dispose of outer gloves in specially marked container. Remove inner gloves. Wash hands and face as a minimum and, if necessary, the whole body.

10.6   On those sites where a decontamination unit is required (see Appendix V) this should consist of three distinct sections. The first section entered on leaving the contaminated area should be used for the storage of contaminated overalls, footwear, etc. The second section should provide a high standard of washing facilities with, if necessary, showers for full body washing. The third section should be used for the storage of the clothing that will be used when leaving the site. Toilet facilities should be positioned such that washing can be carried out prior to their use.

10.7   Wash water generated during decontamination of protective clothing and equipment should be transferred to a suitable sealed tank for appropriate disposal.

10.8   Contaminated clothing and equipment should preferably be processed by professional cleaners who have been informed of the nature of the contamination. On no account should contaminated clothing or protective equipment be taken to any residence for washing. Disposable items should be disposed of at a designated and approved location off-site.

10.9   Some codes, standards and sources of information related to protective clothing and equipment are given in Appendix VI.

10.10   Routine inspection and, where appropriate, calibration of monitoring and safety equipment should be carried out. The need to upgrade safety equipment in line with new codes of practice and specifications should also be kept under review.

References

ASSOCIATION OF GEOTECHNICAL SPECIALISTS. *Safety Manual for Investigation Sites*. P.O. Box 250, Camberley, UK, 1992 (a).

ASSOCIATION OF GEOTECHNICAL SPECIALISTS. *Safety Awareness on Investigation Sites*. AGS/S/1/92, P.O. Box 250, Camberley, UK, 1992 (b).

BRITISH DRILLING ASSOCIATION. *Code of Safe Drilling Practice*. P.O. Box 113, Brentwood, UK, 1992.

BRITISH STANDARDS INSTITUTION. *The Protection of Persons Against Ionising Radiations Arising from any Work Activity*. Approved Code of Practice to the Ionising Radiations Regulations, 1985.

DEPARTMENT OF THE ENVIRONMENT. *Radioactive Substances Act*. HMSO, London, 1960.

DEPARTMENT OF THE ENVIRONMENT. *Health and Safety at Work etc. Act*. HMSO, London, 1974.

DEPARTMENT TO THE ENVIRONMENT. *Environmental Protection Act*. HMSO, London 1990.

HEALTH AND SAFETY EXECUTIVE. *Control of Lead at Work Regulations*. S1, 1980, No. 1248, HMSO, London, 1980.

HEALTH AND SAFETY EXECUTIVE. *Classification, Packaging and Labelling of Dangerous Substances*. HMSO, London, 1984.

HEALTH AND SAFETY EXECUTIVE. *Ionising Radiations Regulations*. S1 1985, No. 1333 HMSO, London, 1985.

HEALTH AND SAFETY EXECUTIVE. *Road Traffic (Carriage of Dangerous Substances in Packages, etc.) Regulations (and Amending Regulations 1989)*. HMSO, London, 1986.

HEALTH AND SAFETY EXECUTIVE. *Control of Asbestos at Work Regulations*. S1, 1987, No. 2115, HMSO, London, 1987.

HEALTH AND SAFETY EXECUTIVE. *Control of Substances Hazardous to Health Regulations*. S1, 1988, No. 1675, HMSO, London, 1988.

HEALTH AND SAFETY EXECUTIVE. *Noise at Work Regulations*. S1, 1989, No. 1790, HMSO, London, 1989. (a)

HEALTH & SAFETY EXECUTIVE. *Electricity at Work Regulations*. S1, 1989, No. 635, HMSO, London, 1989 (b).

HEALTH AND SAFETY EXECUTIVE. *Packaging and Labelling of Dangerous Substances for Conveyance by Road. Approved Code of Practice*. HMSO, London, 1990.

HOBSON D. M. Rational Site Investigations. *Contaminated Land: Problems and Solutions.* Ed. T. Cairney, Blackie, Glasgow, 1993.

INSTITUTION OF CIVIL ENGINEERS. *Conditions of Contract for Ground Investigation.* Thomas Telford, London, 1983.

INSTITUTION OF CIVIL ENGINEERS *et al. Conditions of contract and forms of tender, agreement and bond for use in connection with works of civil engineering construction.* ICE *et al.* London, 5th edition, 1973; 6th edition, 1991.

LORD D. W. Appropriate Site Investigations. *Reclaiming Contaminated Land.* Ed. T. Cairney, Blackie, Glasgow, 1987.

MINISTRY OF AGRICULTURE, FISHERIES AND FOOD. *Preventing the Spread of Plant and Animal Deseases. A Practical Guide.* MAFF Publications, London, 1991.

Suggested reading

ATKINS W.S. & PARTNERS, *Research on Landfill Gas-Monitoring Equipment and Investigation Techniques*. W.S. Atkins & Partners, Epsom, England. KT18 5BW. Report to DOE, November 1988.

BEEVER P.F., *Assessment of Fire Hazards in Contaminated Land*. In *Contaminated Soil* Eds J.W.Assink and W.J. Van den Brink, Martinus Nijhoff, Dordrencht, The Netherlands, pp.515-522, 1986.

BRITISH STANDARDS INSTITUTION, Code of Practice for Site Investigations. The proposed revision of BS.5930 : 1981 is in course of preparation under BSI Sub-Committee B/526/1. BSI, London.

BRITISH STANDARDS INSTITUTION, Guidance on the Preservation and Handling of Samples, BS 6068, 1986.

BRITISH STANDARDS INSTITUTION, Code of Practice for Selection, Installation, Use and Maintenance of Apparatus for the Detection and Measurement of Combustible Gases (other than for mining applications or explosives processing and manufacturing), BS 6959, 1988

BRITISH STANDARDS INSTITUTION, Code of Practice for the Identification of Potentially Contaminated Land and its Investigation, DD.175, 1988.

BUILDING RESEARCH ESTABLISHMENT, Fire And Explosion Hazards Associated with the Development of Contaminated Land, BRE Information Paper 2/87D, 1987.

BUILDING RESEARCH ESTABLISHMENT, Measurement of Gas Emissions from Contaminated Land, 1987.

CAIRNEY T., *Reclaiming Contaminated Land,* Blackie, Glasgow, 1987.

CAIRNEY T., *Contaminated Land : Problems and Solutions,* Blackie Academic & Professional, Glasgow, 1993.

CAMPBELL D., Detecting the Dangers. *Surveyor,* pp.14-15, 20th October 1988.

DEPARTMENT OF THE ENVIRONMENT, Control of Pollution Act and Associated Regulations. HMSO, London, 1974.

DEPARTMENT OF THE ENVIRONMENT, Radioactive Substances Act, 1960 : A Guide to the Administration of the Act. HMSO, London, 1982.

DEPARTMENT OF THE ENVIRONMENT, Special Waste. Waste Management Paper No. 23. HMSO, London, 1982.

DEPARTMENT OF THE ENVIRONMENT, Landfilling Wastes. Waste Management Paper No. 26. A Technical Memorandum for the Disposal of Wastes on Landfill Sites. HMSO, London, 1986.

DEPARTMENT OF THE ENVIRONMENT, The Control of Landfill Gas. Waste Management Paper No. 27, HMSO, London, 1991.

DEPARTMENT OF THE ENVIRONMENT, Survey of Contaminated Land in Wales, HMSO, London, 1988.

EUROPEAN TECHNICAL COMMITTEE 8, Geotechnics of Landfill Design and Remedial Works - Technical Recommendations GLR, Ernst and Sohn, Berlin, 1993.

HEALTH AND SAFETY COMMISSION, Control of Lead at Work : Approved Code of Practice, HMSO, London, 1985.

HEALTH AND SAFETY COMMISSION, Personal Protective Equipment at Work - Proposals for Regulations and Guidance, London, 1991.

HEALTH AND SAFETY EXECUTIVE, Control of Pollution Act, The Disposal of Special Wastes SI 1980 No. 1709, London, 1980.

HEALTH AND SAFETY EXECUTIVE, Work with Asbestos Insulation and Asbestos Coating and Asbestos Insulating Board : Approved Code of Practice, HMSO, London, 1988

HEALTH AND SAFETY EXECUTIVE, COSHH Assessments : A Step by Step Guide to Assessments and the Skills Needed for it, Control of Substances Hazardous to Health Regulations. HMSO, London, 1988.

HEALTH AND SAFETY EXECUTIVE, First Aid at Work : Approved Code of Practice and Guidance. HMSO, London, 1990.

HEALTH AND SAFETY EXECUTIVE, Protection of Works and the General Public during Development of Contaminated Land, 1991.

HEALTH AND SAFETY EXECUTIVE, Guidance Notes and Booklets : Environmental Hygiene Series (EH), General Series (GS), Methods for the Determination of Hazardous Subsance Series (MDHS) and Health and Safety : Regulations Booklets (HS(R)).

HEALTH AND SAFETY EXECUTIVE, Asbestos – Exposure Limits and Measurement of Airborne Dust Concentrations, Guidance Note EH.10, 1990.

HEALTH AND SAFETY EXECUTIVE, Ventilation of the Workplace, Guidance Note EH.22, 1988.

HEALTH AND SAFETY EXECUTIVE, Control of Lead : Outside Workers, Guidance Note EH.29, 1981.

HEALTH AND SAFETY EXECUTIVE, Occupational Exposure Limits, Guidance Note EH.40/92, 1991.

HEALTH AND SAFETY EXECUTIVE, Respiratory Protective Equipment for Use against Asbestos, Guidance Note EH.41, 1985.

HEALTH AND SAFETY EXECUTIVE, Monitoring Strategies for Toxic Substances, Guidance Note EH.42, 1989.

HEALTH AND SAFETY EXECUTIVE, Provision, Use And Maintenance of Hygiene Facilities for Work with Asbestos Insulation and Coatings, Guidance Note EH.47, 1990.

HEALTH AND SAFETY EXECUTIVE, Training Operatives and Supervisors for Work with Asbestos Insulation and Coatings, Guidance Note EH.50, 1988.

HEALTH AND SAFETY EXECUTIVE, Removal Techniques and Associated Waste Handling for Asbestos Insulation, Coatings and Insulating Board, Guidance Note EH.52, 1989.

HEALTH AND SAFETY EXECUTIVE, Entry into Confined Spaces, Guidance Note GS.5, 1977.

HEALTH AND SAFETY EXECUTIVE, First Aid at Work, HS(R) Booklet, 1981.

HEALTH AND SAFETY EXECUTIVE, Protective Clothing, Changing and Washing Facilities for Asbestos, Guidance Booklet 3.

INSTITUTE OF WASTE MANAGEMENT, Monitoring of Landfill Gas, 1989.

INTERDEPARTMENTAL COMMITTEE ON THE RE-DEVELOPMENT OF CONTAMINATED LAND, Notes on the Development and After-Use of Landfill Sites. Guidance Note 17/78, 8th Edition, December 1990.

INTERDEPARTMENTAL COMMITTEE ON THE RE-DEVELOPMENT OF CONTAMINATED LAND, Notes on the Redevelopment of Gas Works Sites, Guidance Note 18/79, 5th Edition, April 1986.

INTERDEPARTMENTAL COMMITTEE ON THE RE-DEVELOPMENT OF CONTAMINATED LAND, Notes on the Redevelopment of Sewage Works and Farms. Guidance Note 23/79, 2nd Edition, November 1983.

INTERDEPARTMENTAL COMMITTEE ON THE RE-DEVELOPMENT OF CONTAMINATED LAND, Notes on the Redevelopment of Scrap Yards and Similar Sites. Guidance Note 42/80, 2nd Edition, October 1983.

INTERDEPARTMENTAL COMMITTEE ON THE RE-DEVELOPMENT OF CONTAMINATED LAND, Guidance on the Assessment and Redevelopment of Contaminated Land. Guidance Note 59/83, 2nd Edition, July 1987.

INTERDEPARTMENTAL COMMITTEE ON THE RE-DEVELOPMENT OF CONTAMINATED LAND, Notes on the Fire Hazards of Contaminated Land. Guidance Note 61/84, 2nd Edition, July 1986.

INTERDEPARTMENTAL COMMITTEE ON THE RE-DEVELOPMENT OF CONTAMINATED LAND, Asbestos on Contaminated Sites. Guidance Note 64/85, 2nd Edition, October 1990.

JONES D.L., CROWCROFT P. and PRITCHARD B.N., Design of a Motorway Service Station on a Landfill Site. *Proceedings of 11th International GRCDA Landfill Gas Symposium,* Houston, Texas. Publication No. GLFG-0016 from GRCDA, P.O.Box 7219, Silver Spring, MD.20920, U.S.A.

LINGWOOD P. and TANKARD J., Safety on Risky Land. *Surveyor,* pp.16-18, 20th October, 1988.

PIDGEON N.F., BLOCKLEY D.I. and TURNER B.A., Site Investigations – Lessons from a Late Discovery of Hazardous Waste. *Structural Engineer,* pp.311-315, October 1988.

MORGAN, H. and SIMMS, D.L., Setting Trigger Concentrations for Contaminated Land. In Vol. 1 of *Contaminated Soil '88,* Second International TNO Conference on Contaminated Soil, Hamburg, 11– 15th April 1988.

SIMMS D.L. and BECKET M.J., Contaminated Land : Setting Trigger Concentrations. *Science of the Total Environment,* Vol. 65, pp.121–134, 1987.

SIMMS D.L., Towards a Scientific Basis for Regulating Lead Contamination. *Science of the Total Environment,* Vol. 58, pp.209-224, 1986.

WHYTE I.L. and PEACOCK W.S., Risk Analysis Applied to the Investigation of Marginal Land. *Polluted & Marginal Land '90.* EngineeringTechnics Press, pp.1-5, 1990.

WILSON D.C.and STEVENS C., Problems Arising from the Redevelopment of Gas Works and Similar Sites. 2nd Edition, HMSO, London, 1988.

YOUNG P.J., Portable Gas Detection Instrumentation. In *Proceedings of UK DOE/US DOE Conference on Energy from Landfill Gas,* Solihull, pp.395-403, 1986.

Appendix I: Boring and drilling plant and methods

Solid stem continuous flight auger drilling   *A.1*   The drilling rig comprises a drill mast, normally 3 to 6m high, and a hydraulically powered rotating continuous flight auger. The rig is normally mounted on a truck or a low ground-bearing-pressure tractor vehicle. The arisings from the borehole are brought to the surface by the auger flights, which are normally 1.5 or 3 m in length. The technique does not require a flushing medium such as water or air. Boreholes can deviate from the perpendicular depending upon the nature of waste or ground material.

The ability of this technique to penetrate or overcome obstructions depends upon the ground conditions, torque of rotary head and weight on augers. Only purpose-designed plant should be used when employing augering techniques. Fatal accidents have occurred when using low-torque high-speed drills which are not designed to enable the technique to be properly executed owing to the operating controls and torque/rotational speed characteristics of the rig. Following completion of the drilling operation the auger has to be withdrawn from the hole before the permanent materials of the borehole can be installed. This can sometimes lead to borehole instability, particularly in saturated ground.

Hollow stem continuous flight auger drilling   *A.2*   This system of drilling is very similar to solid stem auger drilling, but it incorporates a hollow tube through which sampling, testing and placement of permanent borehole instrumentation may be achieved. The technique does not require water or air flushing media, thus avoiding in some cases cross-contamination of boreholes solids or fluids and minimal surface contamination.

During drilling a temporary plug is 'latched' into the drill bit on the leading length of auger. Prior to in situ testing, sampling or installation of permanent materials, the plug may be withdrawn by the drill rods or a wireline recovery tool. The plug is then replaced to continue augering after completion of testing and sampling.

On completion of drilling and following installation of any permanent materials, the auger can be withdrawn over the permanent materials.

Cable percussion boring (shell and auger)   *A.3*   This type of boring rig comprises a winch which is normally powered by a diesel engine and an A-frame or derrick about 6 m in height. The legs of the derrick normally fold down to form a single trailer that can be towed by a four-wheel-drive vehicle onto the site.

The boring principle is simple and is effected by dropping a weighted cutting tool or a shell into the ground. To achieve progress it is sometimes necessary to add water to the borehole during boring. Temporary steel casing is usually inserted to ensure that the borehole remains stable during boring operations. Casing is not always required when drilling in unsaturated well-compacted granular materials or in cohesive materials. This technique is relatively cheap, although obstructions often cannot be overcome by chiselling, and hence additional alternative holes have to be bored.

Large-diameter single-tube barrel A.4 This technique is normally carried out by a larger hydraulic top drive rotary rig mounted on a tractor or truck chassis. A single-tube large-diameter core barrel fitted with a hardened shoe is attached to the high-torque rotary head by large-diameter drill rods. No flushing medium is required. Using this method a perpendicular, clean hole is formed which aids the installation of permanent materials. Borehole stability and sample/core recovery is, however, more difficult in saturated ground.

Conventional rotary drilling A.5 These techniques include rotary coring, rotary open-holing and rotary percussion drilling using conventional methods and standard equipment. They can be used on sites adjacent to landfills to enable the installation of monitoring points or wells, or in contaminated sites where ground and groundwater conditions and the objectives of the project suit these techniques. A flushing medium is required, such as water, air, foam or polymer, etc.

Single flight auger A.6 This technique is employed only on sites where large-diameter holes (1000 mm) are required. The rig employed is either a crawler or truck chassis, supporting a 15 to 20 m high jib or mast fitted with a high-torque rotary table or head driving a telescopic 'kelly bar'. This single flight auger is attached to the kelly, and by a combination of rotation and weight the auger is advanced into the ground. Each pass or bite of the auger is short to enable removal of the material from the auger flights and avoid any jamming in the hole. Although the costs are high to employ this type of plant and equipment the power available allows large-diameter holes to be drilled in difficult ground conditions.

Appendix II: Additional items which could be included in the Bill of Quantities to cover landfills and contaminated land

Item	Unit	Quantity	Rate	Amount
Carry out desk study of previous contaminative uses of the site	Sum			
Provision of environmental specialist/chemist full time on site	Day			
Mobilisation of site safety equipment for GREEN category site	Sum			
Mobilisation of site safety equipment for YELLOW category site	Sum			
Mobilisation of site safety equipment for RED category site	Sum			
Maintenance on site of safety equipment for GREEN category site	Week			
Maintenance on site of safety equipment for YELLOW category site	Week			
Maintenance on site of safety equipment for RED category site	Week			
Emergency analytical testing of unexpected materials encountered where this is required in order to prevent danger to health or where it affects decisions on safety (additional to any testing already included in the Contract). Rates to be agreed	Provisional sum			
Provision of special insurance relating to working on contaminated land or landfill sites and in accordance with the Conditions of Contact	Sum			
Compliance with the special requirements of	Sum			
Extra over drilling or cable tool boring items for the use of safety equipment for category YELLOW site	Day			
Extra over drilling or cable tool boring items for the use of safety equipment for category RED site	Day			
Disposal of samples off site arising from a category YELLOW site	Provisional sum			
Disposal of samples off site arising from a category RED site	Provisional sum			
Decontamination of equipment at end of field work for a category YELLOW site	Sum			
Decontamination of equipment at end of field work for a category RED site	Sum			

Guidelines for the safe investigation by drilling of landfills and contaminated land. Thomas Telford, London, 1993

Appendix III: Site categorisation

Site designation	Broad description
GREEN	Subsoil, topsoil, hardcore, bricks, stone, concrete, clay, excavated road materials, glass, ceramics, abrasives, etc. Wood, paper, cardboard, plastics, metals, wool, cork, ash, clinker, cement, etc. Note: there is a possibility that bonded asbestos could be contained in otherwise inert areas
YELLOW	Waste food, vegetable matter, floor sweepings, household waste, animal carcasses, sludge, trees, bushes, garden waste, leather, etc. Rubber and latex, tyres, epoxy resin, electrical fittings, soaps, cosmetics, non-toxic metal and organic compounds, tar, pitch, bitumen, solidified wastes, fuel ash, silica dust, etc.
RED	All substances that could subject persons and animals to risk of death, injury or impairment of health Wide range of chemicals, toxic metal and organic compounds, etc.; pharmaceutical and veterinary wastes, phenols, medical products, solvents, beryllium, micro-organisms, asbestos, thiocyanates, clyanides, dye stuffs, etc. Hydrocarbons, peroxides, chlorates, flammable and explosive materials; materials that are particularly corrosive or carcinogenic, etc.

Notes

It should be borne in mind that indiscriminate dumping may have taken place on a particular landfill or contaminated site, and therefore the above categorisation should be treated as a guide only to determining operational procedures.

Landfill sites licensed to accept asbestos waste or other sites where significant deposits of bound or unbound asbestos occur justifiably have a RED designation, warranting the highest level of caution. However, many contaminated sites may have only very small quantities of asbestos, often present as asbestos cement, which (while presenting a hazard) may not in themselves warrant the highest level of protection. In these cases it may be sufficient simply to add mains water to the borehole to prevent asbestos fibres becoming airborne and hence available for inhalation, and to wear disposable 'paper masks suitable for low levels of asbestos.

The presence of radioactive materials on a site has not been included in the above categorisation because these are the subject of the Radioactive Substances Act 1960, The Ionising Radiations Regulations 1985 and the Approved Code of Practice to the Regulations entitled *The Protection of Persons Against Ionising Radiations Arising From any Work Activity*.

The majority of dye stuffs are likely to be in the YELLOW category. However, there is a variety of base materials that have been used for the manufacture of dyes and it is possible that some of these, when in concentrated form, could be sufficiently toxic to require a RED designation. Therefore, unless specific information is available regarding composition, the presence of dye stuffs will justify a RED designation.

In those situations where a desk study has not been carried out, or the desk study has not revealed sufficient information, then the site should be given an automatic RED designation.

Contract details	
Project name	
Employer	
Consulting engineer/architect	

Is any of the investigation over land thought/known to contain hazardous materials?	Yes/No

If Yes

1. Do the contract documents define the area thought/known to contain hazardous materials?	Yes/No

2. Give details of where hazardous materials may be found

_____

_____

_____

_____

_____

_____

_____

_____

_____

_____

_____

3. Has any hazard assessment been carried out for this site? If so, by whom?	Yes/No

_____

4. Are details of possible hazardous materials contained in the contract documentation?	Yes/No
5. Is a hazard assessment available?	Yes/No

Form completed by	*Print name*
Date	
On behalf of	*Print organisation*
Signature	

Guidelines for the safe investigation by drilling of landfills and contaminated land. Thomas Telford, London, 1993

Specific details of areas where made ground/hazardous materials are expected

The following information is required for each area involved

Project name _____

Location _____

Exploratory hole nos. or area _____

Grid reference (if known) _____

Present owner/tenant/operator _____

Previous owner _____

Previous use of site, if any _____

Brief description of nature of hazard expected _____

_____

Has the site ever been used for landfill/tipping? | Yes/No

If so give details and material thought to have been placed on site _____

_____

Has the site been licensed? | Yes/No

If so give details _____

_____

Is the license current | Yes/No

Assessment of this part of the site under SISG Classification (circle as appropriate) | RED YELLOW GREEN

Special precautions to be taken — as SISG recommendation

Additional precautions advised _____

_____

_____

For checklist of hazards expected see Sheet 3

Form completed by	*Print name*
Date	
On behalf of	*Print organisation*
Signature	

Checklist of hazards expected — tick as appropriate
If asterisked boxes are ticked please give more details

1 Methane	
2 Carbon dioxide	
3 Hydrogen sulphide	
4 Other gases	*
5 Heavy metals	*
6 Polychlorinatedbiphenyls (PCB)	
7 Hydrocarbons	*
8 Phenol	
9 Pesticides	*
10 Asbestos	
11 Domestic refuse	
12 Industrial waste	
13 pH conditions	*
14 Coal tars/polynuclear aromatic hydrocarbons (PAH)	
15 Cyanide	
16 Combustibility hazards (e.g. coal dust)	
17 Radioactivity	*
18 Weil's Disease (rats)	
19 Other contaminants	*

Extra details

_____

_____

_____

_____

_____

_____

Form completed by	*Print name*
Date	
On behalf of	*Print organisation*
Signature	

Appendix V: Site designation/site safety equipment

Item	Site designation		
	GREEN	YELLOW	RED
Personal protective equipment			
Hard hat	*	*	*
Eye protection		*	*
Face shield		*	*
Hand protection	*	*	*
Overalls	*	*	
Disposable overalls			*
Waterproofs	*	*	
Disposable waterproofs			*
Industrial boots	*	*	*
Wellington boots with sole and toe protections	*	*	*
Respiratory equipment		*	*
Site equipment/services			
Mobile telephone (outside contaminated area)		*	*
Ropes, cones and barriers			*
Safety/warning signs	*	*	*
Clean water supply	*	*	*
Changing room/washing facilities		*	*
Decontamination unit/washing facilities			*
Emergency equipment			
Fire extinguisher	*	*	*
Fire blanket	*	*	*
First aid kit	*	*	*

Gas detection/gas monitoring equipment (where required)		
Methane (flammable gas)	Hydrogen sulphide	Other gases and
Carbon dioxide	Oxygen deficiency	fumes

Drilling plant/safety equipment (where required)
Spark arrestors and automatic air intake shutdown valves
Air blower
Vertical exhaust stacks and air intakes should be located not less than 1.5 m above ground level

Appendix VI: Protective clothing and equipment — relevant Codes, Standards and information

The following is intended as a guide only and may not include all items that will be required on a particular site.

Item	Relevant Code/Standard
Ear defenders	BS 6344 Noise at Work Regulations 1989
Eye protection	BS 2092 BS 679 BS 1542 Protection of Eyes Regulations 1989
Head protection	BS 5240 Construction (Head Protection) Regulations 1989
Hand protection	BS 1651
Body protection	BS 2823 BS 6629 BS 7184
Foot protection	BS 1870
Respiratory protection	BS 2091 BS 4555 BS 6016 BS 7355 BS 7356 BS EN 146 BS EN 149

Notes

Respiratory Protective Equipment (RPE) — RPE standards are currently being brought into line with European Standards. It is important to purchase, wherever possible, equipment conforming to the European Norm (EN).

Respiratory Protective Equipment — Legislative Requirements and List of HSE Approved Standards and Type Approved Equipment: Second Edition: 1991.

Respiratory Protective Equipment — A Practical Guide for Users, HS(G)53: 1990.

For protection against radioactivity reference should be made to HSE Guidance Note EH 53: 1990: Respiratory Protective Equipment For Use Against Airborne Radioactivity.

For protection against asbestos reference should be made to HSE Guidance Note EH 41: 1985: Respiratory Protective Equipment For Use Against Asbestos and to HSE Asbestos Manufacturing Guidance Booklet — Protective Clothing, Changing and Washing Facilities For Asbestos.

Appendix VII: Membership of Site Investigation Steering Group and working panels

Site Investigation Steering Group

Professor G.S. Littlejohn, BSc, PhD, FEng, FICE, FIStructE, FGS, University of Bradford (Chairman)

Mr R. Cater, BSc, CEng, MICE, CGeol, FGS, Hampshire County Council

Professor C.R.I. Clayton, BSc, MSc, DIC, PhD, CEng, MICE, University of Surrey

Mr K.W. Cole, BSc, MSc, CEng, FICE, Arup Geotechnics

Mr G.P. Dean, BSc, CEng, MICE, Oscar Faber Consulting Engineers

Dr M.H. de Freitas, PhD, CGeol, FGS, Imperial College of Science, Technology and Medicine

Mr R.M.C. Driscoll, BSc, MSc, CEng, FICE, Building Research Establishment

Mr J.D. Findlay, MSc, CEng, MICE, FGS, Stent Foundations Ltd.

Mr P.A. Gee, BSc, CEng, FICE, Soil Mechanics Ltd.

Dr D.A. Greenwood, BSc, PhD, CEng, FICE, FGS, Cementation Piling and Foundations Ltd.

Mr J.R. Greenwood, BSc, MEng, CEng, MICE, MIHT, FGS, Travers Morgan

Mr B.S. Hookins, CEng, MICE, Messrs. Scott-White & Hookins

Mr F.M. Jardine, MSc(Eng), Construction Industry Research and Information Association

Mr R.W. Johnson, CEng, FIStructE, National House-Building Council

Mr T.M. Leon, BSc, FRICS, MIQA, Consultant

Dr J.A. Lord, MA(Cantab), CEng, MICE, Arup Geotechnics

Dr D.M. McCann, B.Sc, MSc(Eng), PhD, CGeol, FGS, British Geological Survey

Dr T.W. Mellors, BSc(Eng), MSc, DIC, PhD, CEng, MICE, MIMM, FGS, Consultant

Mr W.H. Pearce, London and Edinburgh Insurance

Mr A. Smith, DArch(Hons), BSc, RIBA, AFAS, ACIArb, Bickerdike Allen and Partners

Mr B.E. Spark, CEng, MICE, MIWEM, Anglian Water Services Ltd.

Mr S.B. Tietz, BSc(Eng), CEng, FICE, S.B. Tietz and Partners

Mr J.R. Wilson, BSc, CEng, MICE, Federation of Civil Engineering Contractors

Mr P.E. Wilson, BSc, CEng, MICE, Department of Transport

Working Panel 1: Geotechnical Awareness Programme

Professor G.S. Littlejohn, BSc, PhD, FEng, FICE, FIStructE, FGS, University of Bradford (Chairman)

Mr K.W. Cole, BSc, MSc, CEng, FICE, Arup Geotechnics

Dr T.W. Mellors, BSc(Eng), MSc, DIC, PhD, CEng, MICE, MIMM, FGS, Consultant

Working Panel 2: Specification for Ground Investigation

Mr J.R. Greenwood, BSc, MEng, CEng, MICE, MIHT, FGS, Travers Morgan (Chairman)

Mr M.I. Cobbe, BSc, CEng, MICE, MIHT, FGS, M.J. Carter Associates Ltd.

Mr J.H. Charman, BSc, CEng, CGeol, MICE, MIMM, FGS, Engineering Geology Ltd.

Mr J.M. McEntee, BSc, CEng, FICE, Consultant

Mr R.W. Skinner, Foundation and Exploration Services Ltd.

Mr P.E. Wilson, BSc, CEng, MICE, Department of Transport

Working Panel 3: Procurement of Site Investigation	Professor C.R.I. Clayton, BSc, MSc, DIC, PhD, CEng, MICE, University of Surrey (Chairman) Mr N. Flesher, FRICS, Laing/GTE Joint Venture Mr D.G.S. Harman, BSc, CGeol, FGS, Consultant Dr L.M. Lake, MSc, DIC, PhD, CEng, FICE, MIMM, FGS, Mott MacDonald Mr R.L. Sanders, MSc, DIC,CEng, MIMM, FIHT, FGS, Babtie Geotechnical Ltd. Mr J.A. Scarrow, BSc, MSc, Soil Mechanics Ltd. Mr A. Smith, DArch(Hons), BSc, RIBA, AFAS, ACIArb, Bickerdike Allen and Partners
Working Panel 4: Planning of Site Investigation	Mr R.M.C. Driscoll, BSc, MSc, CEng, FICE, Building Research Establishment (Chairman) Mr G.P.Dean, BSc, CEng, MICE, Oscar Faber Consulting Engineers Dr M.H. de Freitas, PhD, CGeol, FGS, Imperial College of Science, Technology and Medicine Mr G.W. Herrick, Department of Transport Mr J.L. Hislam, BSc, MPhil,CEng, FICE, MASCE, Terresearch Ltd. Mr S. Quarrell, BSc, MSc, CEng, MICE, Soil Consultants Ltd. Dr M. Stroud, MA(Cantab), PhD, CEng, MICE, Arup Geotechnics
Corresponding Members	Mr K. Ansell, Sir Robert McAlpine Dr B.R. Marker, BSc, PhD, Department of the Environment
Working Panel 5: Quality Management of Site Investigation	Dr D.A. Greenwood, BSc, PhD, FICE, FGS, Cementation Piling and Foundations Ltd. (Chairman) Ms R. Allington, BSc, MSc, CEng, MIMM, FGS, Geoffrey Walton & Partners Mr T. Carbray, CEng, FICE, MIQA, Messrs.Sandberg Mr A.J.Cowan, CEng, MICE. MIQA, Williamson QA Mr R.W. Dowell, CGeol, FGS, Exploration Associates Ltd. Mr J.C. Haynes, BSc(Eng), CEng, MICE, MIStructE, MCIOB, National House-Building Council Mr R. Lung, BSc, MPhil, MSc, CEng, MICE, MIStructE, Department of Transport Mr P.H. Oldham, CEng, FICE, MIQA, Gillott Sawyer Associates
British Drilling Association Working Panel: Safe Drilling of Landfills and Contaminated Land	Mr R.W. Skinner, Foundation and Exploration Services Mr J.A. Scarrow, MSc, BSc, Soil Mechanics Ltd. Professor G.S. Littlejohn, BSc, PhD,FEng, FICE,FIStructE, FGS, University of Bradford in conjunction with C.L. Associates, Environmental Specialists